Introduction

The sea lochs of Scotland are very special places both for the people who live around their shores and the magnificent wildlife which depends on their protected waters.

The spectacular scenery of the highlands and islands of Scotland attracts many visitors each year. Steep-sided mountains and a rugged landscape contrast dramatically with tranquil, water-filled valleys.

There are over a hundred sea lochs on the west coast and islands of Scotland. Many are very deep, long and narrow, winding many kilometres inland between steep-sided mountains like sinuous fingers of the sea. These are known as fjords. Other sea lochs, known as fjards, are broad and shallow, dotted with many small islands and basins connected by narrows.

How were sea lochs formed?

Between 2.5 million and 10,000 years ago, much of Scotland was intermittently covered by great sheets of ice which fashioned the landscape of Scotland which we see today.

Fjords:

In the mountainous areas of the west coast, glaciers flowed through the steep-sided river valleys, scouring deep basins in the valley floor as they went. Eventually the climate warmed and the ice receded. Sea levels rose, flooding some of the basins with seawater, thus creating the fjordic sea lochs we see today. In some places, such as Loch Tarbert on Jura there are signs of past sea level changes in the old shorelines at up to 40 metres above the present sea level. There is also evidence, in marine shells found in the glacial deposits, which shows that Loch Lomond was a sea loch only 12,000 years ago. As the last ice advance retreated, it deposited moraines which combined with dropping sea levels cut off Loch Lomond and it became the freshwater loch we see today.

Where the ice met harder rocks, or melted on reaching the sea or lower ground, rock and boulder ridges resulted. These now form shallow areas, or sills, between deeper basins and at the seaward entrance to many sea lochs.

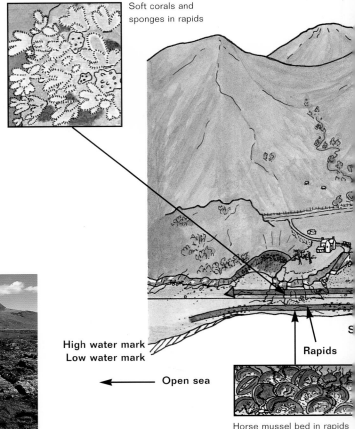

Soft corals and sponges in rapids

High water mark
Low water mark

Open sea

Rapids

Horse mussel bed in rapids

Loch Scridain and Ben More

Fjordic sealoch - Diagram to show shape, seabed type and water movement

Fjordic landscape with deep sealoch basin formed by erosive force of glaciers moving down from the mountains

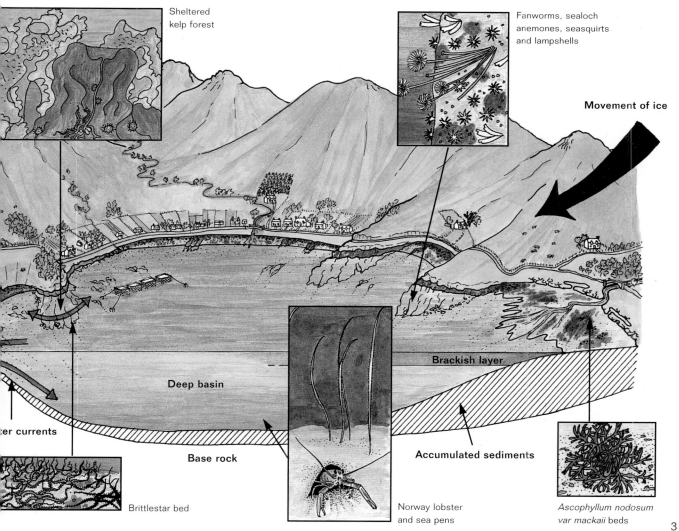

Sheltered kelp forest

Fanworms, sealoch anemones, seasquirts and lampshells

Movement of ice

Brackish layer

Deep basin

er currents

Base rock

Accumulated sediments

Brittlestar bed

Norway lobster and sea pens

Ascophyllum nodosum var mackaii beds

3

Fjards:

In low-lying areas glaciation has resulted in a very different landscape. The ice sheets moved slowly and evenly over the land, eroding small basins and leaving mounds of harder rock. The resulting knob and lochan landscape is characteristic of many parts of the Western Isles. Flooding by the sea resulted in shallow, complex fjardic sea lochs with a mosaic of small, shallow basins separated by sills and tidal rapids in the narrows between the numerous small islands.

Loch Laxford, a mosaic of islands, shallow basins and tidal rapids

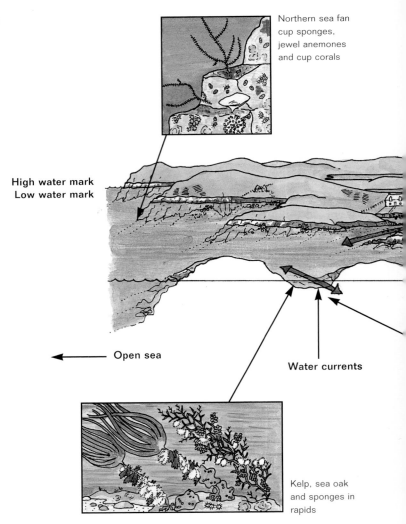

Northern sea fan cup sponges, jewel anemones and cup corals

High water mark
Low water mark

Open sea

Water currents

Kelp, sea oak and sponges in rapids

Fjardic sealoch - Diagram to show shape, seabed type and water movement

'Knob and Lochan' landscape formed by horizontal movement of ice sheet

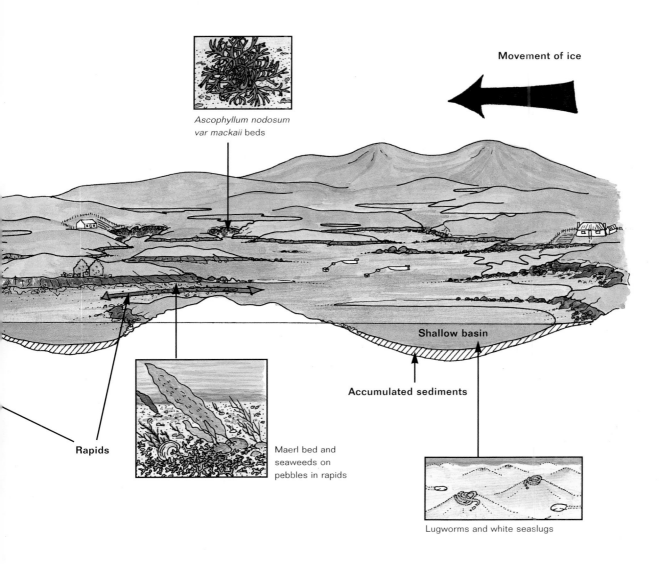

Ascophyllum nodosum
var mackaii beds

Movement of ice

Shallow basin

Accumulated sediments

Rapids

Maerl bed and
seaweeds on
pebbles in rapids

Lugworms and white seaslugs

Painted goby

The sea anemone
(*Protanthea simplex*)

Dead man's fingers

Bloody Henry starfish
on sponge

7

Seashore life

Unlike the extensive areas of mud flat characteristic of sheltered inlets in other parts of Britain, sea loch shores are typically a mixture of steep-sided rock or more gently sloping boulders and shingle. Pockets of mud and sand do occur in sheltered bays, but these are often overlain by shingle and boulders. The rich variety of life found especially at low water makes them ideal and exciting places to investigate with the tantalising promise of finding something rare or unusual.

Rocky shores

At low tide, life on rocky shores shows as bands of different colours and textures. Animals and plants are arranged in distinctive zones starting at the very top of the shore with grey, yellow and black lichens, looking more like splashes of paint than plants. Much of the mid-shore is covered with a variety of brown seaweeds, arranged in bands down the shore - channelled wrack, followed by spiral wrack, then a mixture of egg wrack and bladder wrack. On the lower shore serrated wrack is often covered with small, orange sea squirts or tiny, coiled, white worm tubes. Kelp plants, large brown seaweed with wide, slippery fronds, are exposed only on the lowest tides at the very bottom of the shore.

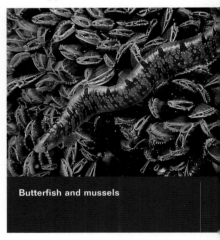

Butterfish and mussels

Loch Scavaig near Elgol

8

Furbelows kelp

On exposed headlands or steeper rocks this zonation is most distinctive with the upper black lichen band contrasting with the rough coat of white barnacles below interspersed with patches of dark blue mussels, often dotted with white dog whelks preying on them. Limpets cling tenaciously to the rocks, and various kinds of winkles are everywhere, grazing on larger seaweeds and the seaweed film on rocks.

Seaweed zonation exposed at low tide, Strome

Because sea lochs are so sheltered, quite small stones may remain unturned by waves and support lichen and seaweed growth. Amphipods, which are small lively relatives of prawns and shrimps occur in large numbers under stones together with green shore crabs and many other species.

Colourful sponges, sea firs and sea anemones thrive in the dampness of rock overhangs sheltered by seaweeds. Several eel-like fish are common on sea loch shores, hiding under seaweeds and stones while the tide is out. Butterfish, with their distinctive light-ringed dark spots, and viviparous (producing live young rather than eggs) blennies can be found on most shores.

Five types of seaweed commonly found on the rocky shores of sea lochs

1. Channelled wrack
2. Spiral wrack
3. Egg/knotted wrack
4. Bladder wrack
5. Serrated wrack

Sediment shores

In most sea lochs there are areas of mud or muddy sand, where the tell-tale toothpaste-like casts of lugworms create a miniature, almost lunar landscape of mounds and craters. The intricate branched tubes of sandmason worms, beautifully built of sand grains, stick up through the sand at the bottom of the shore. Nearer the top of the shore, tiny black spire snails graze the surface of the sand or mud leaving tortuous tracks in their wake.

Other animals live buried in sand or mud. These include various bivalve molluscs, especially cockles, a range of worms, amphipods and sea potatoes (a burrowing sea urchin).

Unattached seaweed, *Ascophlylum nodosum var mackaii* which is largely restricted to sea lochs

Sandmason worm tube sticking up through the sand

Common mussels grow to a large size, forming dense and extensive beds where freshwater streams spread out over the shingle shores, or on very shallow sills where brackish surface water flows at low tide. The extreme shelter and variable salinity characteristic of many sea lochs, provide perfect conditions for two unusual species of brown seaweed. A much-branched, almost bladderless form of egg wrack grows unattached in wig-sized clumps in places where there is no danger of removal by waves or tides. The smallest wrack of all, moss wrack, grows less than a centimetre tall at the top of very sheltered shores, giving the saltmarsh turf a gingery-brown hue from a distance.

Underwater life

The underwater world of sea lochs is remarkable, populated by a great diversity of strange and colourful animals and plants extending from the clear shallows of only a few metres to murky depths in excess of 200 metres where complete and utter darkness prevails. It is only recently, with the development of SCUBA diving, that the upper regions of this underwater world has been accessible but even today only a few of people have experienced the thrill of a dive. SCUBA divers cannot dive much below 50 metres and it is only very recently that technology has enabled us to explore the deeper areas using Remote Operated Vehicles (ROVs).

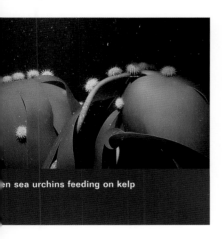

sea urchins feeding on kelp

The large, slippery, brown kelps which can sometimes be seen on the lowest tides, mark the top edge of a great kelp forest which extends underwater all around the coast of Britain wherever there are suitable hard surfaces for the kelp to attach to.

The stiff-stemmed kelp, Cuvie *Laminaria hyperborea*, with its split, palm-like frond grows best in strong water movement and provides a sheltered home and food for a wide variety of marine animals and plants living on the seabed and on the kelp itself.

In the quieter waters inside sea lochs, another kelp, sugar kelp *(Laminaria saccharina)* with an undivided, crinkly frond, gradually takes over as the dominant species. The fronds of sugar kelp lie across the seabed, shading the silty rocks beneath. Often the rock has a crust of hard, pink coralline seaweed and animal life is confined to a few sea squirts, squat lobsters and brittlestars in crevices.

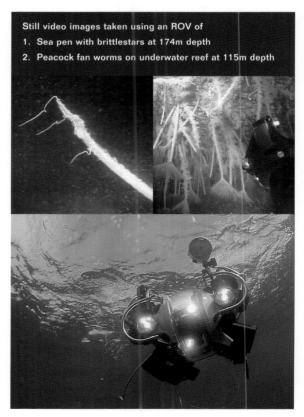

Still video images taken using an ROV of
1. Sea pen with brittlestars at 174m depth
2. Peacock fan worms on underwater reef at 115m depth

ROV at surface

11

Tidal rapids

Tidal rapids are the most species-rich parts of sea lochs and often contain several different habitats and communities in a small area. The seabed looks like a mass of plant growth, but often these are animals in disguise with plant-like names such as sea anemones, sea firs and sea mosses (otherwise known as sea mats). Just as plants spread out branches and leaves to collect the maximum amount of light from the sun, these animals spread out arms and tentacles to capture small particles carried on the water currents. A range of mobile animals such as fish, sea urchins, starfish, squat lobsters and hermit crabs graze on the attached animals and plants or search for other mobile prey.

In the shallow tidal rapids, dense sea firs and sea mats grow beneath tall kelp plants and a large brown seaweed, the sea oak (*Halidrys siliquosa*). Magnificent sponges, particularly the green and yellow breadcrumb sponge, often wrap around kelp holdfasts. Myriads of tiny ghost shrimps hang all around. Small multicoloured anemones nestle in crevices and any rock not colonised by animals has a smooth hard living paint of coralline seaweed. In deeper water, dense orange or white soft corals, dead man's fingers, are preyed on by the mushroom-coloured, giant triton seaslug, up to 20 centimetres long, and the red cushion star.

Maerl beds

The mixed seabeds found in many tidal rapids probably represent the remains of glacial moraines from which all fine material has been winnowed out by the water currents. Various sizes of stones have been left among coarse, mobile gravel and support a wide variety of animals living on, between and under stones. Sea firs, brittlestars, butterfish, squat lobsters and queen scallops all abound while spectacular red and white striped dahlia anemones and sunstars add splashes of startling colour. A variety of exotically coloured seaslugs eat the sea firs and sea mats, and hermit crabs scuttle here, there and everywhere. Other animals need searching for - the elusive Yarrell's blenny for instance with its topknot of tentacles lives hidden in crevices or even in old bottles.

Maerl, or 'Scottish coral', is not a coral at all but rather it is an unusual red seaweed which lives unattached on the sea bed either as a thin living veneer above the mud and sand or in great banks and waves. It has a brittle, calcareous skeleton which is easily damaged by mechanical disturbance such as anchors, trawls or dredges. Maerl grows very slowly, typically only 1 or 2 millimetres per year, so its small twiggy nodules may be many years old. Although maerl beds are a relatively rare habitat, they are very important for the survival of many small animals and the juvenile stages of many others including various commercial species which hide and shelter amongst the nodules.

Maerl

Coral beach, Skye, maerl remnants washed ashore

Brittlestar beds in Loch Sunart

Brittlestar beds

In some places the seabed writhes with a living mat of brittlestars. These can be as dense as up to 2,000 brittlestars per metre square to the exclusion of most other animals. If currents become too strong and the brittlestars are in danger of being swept away, they link arms with their neighbours and lie flat to the seabed, forming a living carpet. Brittlestar beds can also be found in areas of less extreme water currents such as headlands inside sea lochs.

Living reefs

Horse mussels, similar to but larger than the common blue mussel, bind to each other and to stones and shells with tough threads forming a platform for many other animals, small seaweeds and even kelps. The beautiful file shell or flame shell performs the same service by building a nest of shells, stones and gravel held together by a weft of threads. The flame shell directs a flow of water through its nest, trapping any nutritious material on the spectacular crown of orange tentacles which gives it its name. In Loch Creran another very unusual living reef is found comprising colonies of tube building worms - *Serpula vermicularis.*

Seabed life

Very sheltered, deep (more than 30 metres) bedrock is a special feature of many sea lochs which supports marine life found nowhere else in Britain. At this depth, daylight is either very much reduced or complete darkness prevails, which means that no plants can survive, so animals dominate the communities. Steeper slopes are often covered with sea squirts and small white anemones, neatly spaced just out of reach of their neighbour's stinging tentacles. Bunches of long, muddy tubes made by peacock fan worms stand out from the rock, crowned with delicately beautiful orange and blue feeding fans. Upward facing rock is often covered with a thick layer of silt. Underneath the silt small limpets and chitons are found, while sea firs and large sea squirts hold their bodies above the layer of silt and small brittlestars often crawl over the silty surface.

Football sea squirt *(Diazona violacea)* with the Northern sea fan *(Swiftia pallida)*

The flame shell with its crown of orange tentacles

In deeper water (more than 50 metres), small, two-shelled animals stud the rocks. These are known as lamp shells because of their resemblance to old oil lamps. Having survived almost unchanged for the last 400 million years, these lamp shells are truly 'living fossils'.

Near the entrances to sea lochs a variety of erect sponges of different shapes and colours grow on deep sheltered bedrock together with the white, slender coral known as the Northern sea fan. Rock surfaces may also be studded with the small Devonshire cup coral, a true, solitary coral with a hard, ribbed skeleton.

15

Conger eel

The holes between boulders and cobbles provide ideal homes for mobile animals such as squat lobsters, crabs and fish. The shy, leopard-spot goby looks out for predators while other territorial fish such as the goldsinny, ballan and cuckoo wrasse also retreat to boulder holes. Larger holes may occasionally be occupied by a lobster or conger eel, both active mainly at night. Between and underneath boulders, brittlestars, sea squirts and worms are just a few of the animals found.

The sea pen (*Virgularia mirabilis*)

Seabeds in the shallower parts of sea lochs are often a mixture of mud, sand, gravel and shells. These mixed sediments can be rich in marine life, both on the surface and buried. In the shallowest parts, seaweeds grow on any small pebble or shell, competing with animals such as barnacles, sea firs and sea squirts for space. Hard surfaces on which to grow are at such a premium that the shells of live scallops may be overgrown with seaweeds and other marine growths. Small fish such as sand gobies, dragonets and young flatfish adopt camouflage colours against the sand, lying in wait for the small crustaceans on which they feed while avoiding being eaten themselves.

Many animals lie buried in the sand stretching out tentacles or arms to feed, but withdrawing into the safety of the sediment if disturbed. Burrowing sea anemones, sea pens, worms, sea cucumbers and brittlestars all live like this while some bivalve molluscs are even less conspicuous, showing just a pair of siphons as holes at the surface. Some seldom seen animals move along below the sediment surface looking for buried prey, like the sea mouse (a kind of worm), the elusive pelican's foot shell and the thin leaf-like goosefoot starfish.

The spectacular fireworks anemone
(Pachycerianthus multiplicatus)

In the most sheltered and deepest parts of sea lochs much of the seabed is of soft, deep mud and home to some spectacular and specialised animals found in no other habitat. Seapens are long, white, feather-like animals related to corals, which stick up from the mud and can form dense beds. All three British species grow in sea lochs but most characteristic of deeper water is *Funiculina quadrangularis* which can grow up to a metre tall. In some places it plays host to a brittlestar, *Asteronyx loveni*, which clings on to the upper regions of the seapen using two of its five arms, while the others are left hanging out in the water to capture food particles. The bright orange Norway lobsters excavate wide, U-shaped burrows and sit in the entrance, sometimes accompanied by a small goby which shares the burrow. Perhaps the most spectacular of all mud-living creatures is the fireworks sea anemone, *Pachycerianthus multiplicatus*, which has a crown of kinked, white tentacles up to 30 centimetre across.

Floating life.

In the spring and early summer the clear sea loch waters turn murky green, the result of millions of tiny floating plants and animals - plankton, many of them too small to see without a microscope. The tiny plants bloom in response to increased day length in spring and are food for hosts of tiny animals. Some of these animals live their whole lives in the plankton while others are the young stages of creatures which eventually settle on the seabed. The animals of the plankton can only float in the sunlit layers and are otherwise at the mercy of the wind and currents. The largest and most familiar animals in this plankton are the jellyfish. Sometimes in the summer vast numbers of jellyfish can be concentrated by winds blowing up a loch, and then become stranded at high tide.

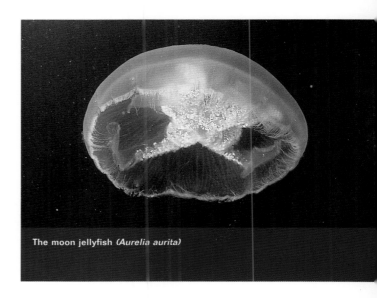

The moon jellyfish (Aurelia aurita)

17

Mammals

The rich marine life of sea lochs provides ample feeding for mammals particularly otters, seals, harbour porpoises and some other cetaceans.

Otters are equally at home in freshwater, brackish or fully marine habitats and the sheltered waters of many sea lochs are ideal for them. They are particularly attracted to rocky shores and shallow water with an extensive seaweed cover where they may be seen hunting their main food, fish and crabs. Otters prefer areas little disturbed by humans with suitable sites for their dens or holts, although they can sometimes be seen on busy slipways. Although protected by legislation, otters have declined in many parts of Britain and Europe but appear still to thriving in western Scotland. However, as a slow breeding, low density species they are vulnerable to any factors which might cause sudden population changes.

At first glance the North American mink might be mistaken for a small otter. Originally bred for their fur, escapees from mink farms now live wild in various parts of Scotland occupying similar territory along waterways and sea loch shores to otters. Mink are ferocious predators of other small mammals and birds - ground nesting birds are particularly vulnerable to mink predation, as well as fish.

Both common and grey seals live on the west coast of Scotland, but common seals are more likely to be seen inside sea lochs, particularly near the entrance and on offshore islands and skerries. Common seals are the smaller of the two species and are best distinguished by their slightly up-turned nose, like a Labrador dog in profile, compared to grey seals which have a longer straight profile or rather 'Roman nose' in the larger males. Seals are attracted to fishfarms, both by the wild fish which congregate around them to eat any surplus fishfood and by the captive salmon. Seals will attack salmon through the mesh of fish cages and anti-predators nets have to be used on the outside of the cages to deter them.

Although cetaceans (dolphins, porpoises and whales) are more often seen in open water, harbour porpoises are frequent visitors to sea lochs and several species of dolphin also visit regularly. These small cetaceans are accustomed to inshore navigation. Minke, killer and other whales occasionally enter sea lochs but it is thought that these larger animals may have strayed into sea lochs by accident or are themselves sick or accompanying another sick animal.

Birds

Ready food supplies and shelter attract many kinds of birds to sea lochs. Some breed around the sea lochs but many more stay during winter before returning to breeding grounds in colder lands further north. Amongst the most evocative sea loch bird is the grey heron, standing solitary and hunched with spear-like beak ready to strike at fish in the shallows. Herons defend their territories and are often spaced at approximately one kilometre intervals along the shore. The reintroduction of the white-tailed sea eagle means that this magnificent bird can once again be seen soaring above the waters of some of the more remote sea lochs.

Various diving ducks, including eider, goldeneye and merganser are common in some sea lochs. Eider may also breed on offshore islands and feed mainly on mussels, so are attracted to mussel farms.

Sea lochs do not attract the huge numbers of waders found on the extensive mud flats in more open estuaries such as the Moray and Solway Firths. There are a number of typical sea loch species; most often seen are the noisy, red-beaked oystercatchers, curlew with their long, curved beaks, long-legged redshank and small sandpipers.

Herring gulls often feed on sea loch shores dropping sea urchins or whelks from a height onto rocks to break their shells. Other gulls dip and terns plunge dive for shoaling fish near the surface, while shags, cormorants and tysties (black guillemots) swim to the seabed in pursuit of bottom dwelling and shoaling fish.

The grey heron

Sea lochs and people

On a coast where much of the land is relatively unproductive and rugged, the climate relatively inhospitable and the growing season short, sea lochs have long been used to glean a living from the sea and for transport and communication along the coast. A narrow fringe of more productive land around the edge of sea lochs has been important for grazing and growing crops. This subsistence farming, combined with in-shore fishing, supported numerous small communities until the Clearances in the late eighteenth and early nineteenth centuries, when many people were moved out of their homes to make way for sheep. More recently, fish farming and tourism have become important sectors of this fragile economy. A clean and healthy marine and coastal environment is a vital part of the selling power of Highland produce.

Loch Seaforth with fish farm cages in foreground

Fishing

Fishing is an important activity in the sea lochs, predominantly carried out from small inshore boats. Creels are set for Norway lobster (known also as prawns or scampi), velvet crabs, brown crabs, lobsters and squat lobsters. In many places winkles are collected commercially on a small scale and a wide variety of shellfish, including winkles, cockles and mussels are collected for the pot.

The seabed is also trawled for prawns, queen scallops and various fish. Heavy dredges rake the seabed for king scallops, which are also collected by divers. Fishermen hunting other commercial species in the waters off the west coast and Minch occasionally venture into the sea lochs, particularly in bad weather, but in the narrow confines of most of the sea lochs it is difficult to operate and manoeuvre larger vessels.

Sea lochs are important spawning grounds for herring, cod and whiting, and nursery grounds for many fish including herring, sprat, cod, saithe and plaice. To protect these fish spawning and nursery grounds, a number of sea lochs are closed to trawls and dredges for part of the year and a few all year round.

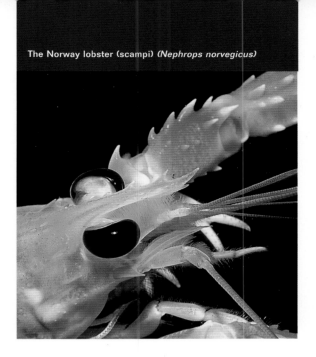

The Norway lobster (scampi) *(Nephrops norvegicus)*

Seaweed harvesting

Seaweed harvesting, another traditional industry, is now much less important to the local economy than it once was, although it is still carried out in some places. Seaweed, mainly kelp, stranded at the top of the shore and known as tangle, has long been collected and spread on the land as a fertiliser and soil conditioner and is a vital source of trace elements. Other seaweeds, in particular egg wrack, are harvested from the shore as the raw material for the alginate industry. Alginates are used in the manufacture of a wide range of food and pharmaceutical products, the brewing industry and also in the dyeing industry.

Fish farming

Fish farming is the recent boom industry of the Highlands. Production of finfish (mainly Atlantic salmon, but increasingly also halibut) which began in the late 1960s has risen to 70,060 tonnes of salmon in 1995 and is projected to continue to increase. This has provided many jobs in an area with limited employment prospects. Shellfish farming of mussels, oysters and scallops is much less profitable, but is perhaps more suited to small scale production and the crofting lifestyle. Total shellfish production in 1995 was 1,252 tonnes.

Since its beginnings the industry has grown so much that almost all the sea lochs on the west coast and the islands have fish farms in them. Shellfish farms have relatively little impact on the marine environment and its wildlife, although there is potential conflict between shellfish farmers and some birds, especially eiders which feed on mussels. There are greater concerns over the potential impact of salmon farms. Concerns include the fouling of the seabed under the farms with fish faeces and uneaten food, although this is relatively localised, and the use of various chemical and antibiotic treatments which may have more long term effects on other marine life including commercial shellfish species.

Tourism

The juxtaposition of sea lochs and mountains creates spectacular scenery. The west coast and Western and Northern Isles are increasingly popular destinations for visitors

who want to tour, walk, sail, dive or simply observe the wildlife in a largely unspoilt environment. Tourism is a growing source of revenue. Interpretation of all aspects of a rich but largely inaccessible marine environment will be important in developing a sustainable recreation industry.

Ports and harbours

All the important west coast harbours and ports, from Glasgow up to Kinlochbervie, are sited in sea lochs or the sounds between islands. Large vessels can safely dock or anchor in their deep, sheltered waters. Ferries continue to be a vital link to many of the offshore islands transporting most goods as well as people. For visitors the ferry journey is often the first experience of the unique atmosphere of the west coast of Scotland in its many moods.

Larger vessels fishing in the Minch or in the deep water off the west of Scotland land their catches in the sheltered ports of Lochinver, Kinlochbervie, Mallaig or Oban, or transfer their catches to the fleet of foreign factory ships or 'Klondykers' to be found anchored in Loch Broom in the late summer.

Small jetties and slipways scatter the shores of the sea lochs; a legacy of times before good Highland roads when most transport between coastal settlements was by sea. Now these jetties are used by fishermen as places to stack their creels, as pick-up points for fish and launch points for small craft.

The importance of sea lochs

Numerous surveys by the Marine Nature Conservation Review and SNH show the amazingly rich and diverse marine life of Scotland's sea lochs, with some species found only in sea lochs. Of 226 different British habitats and their associated animals and plants, otherwise known as biotopes, 90 have been recorded in Scottish sea lochs including records for over 1,700 species of marine invertebrates and seaweeds.

Sea lochs have communities which are not found elsewhere. In particular the rich marine life in tidal rapids and on deep, sheltered rock together with a wide range of other habitats makes the Scottish sea lochs outstanding areas for marine wildlife. Tidal rapids are rare throughout north east Europe, making those in Scottish sea lochs of international importance.

Scotland's sea lochs are very special both for wildlife and people and developing a balanced approach to conserving their special features of interest is vitally important for all.

The semi-enclosed nature of sea lochs makes them vulnerable to various impacts particularly accumulation of pollutants. Too much organic material on the seabed will quickly use up available oxygen and in the absence of water currents or waves to supply more oxygenated water the seabed can become anoxic (lacking in oxygen) killing marine wildlife.

Some of the sea loch marine communities including the maerl beds and seapens are particularly sensitive to mechanical disturbance such as trawling, dredging and anchoring.

Threats to sea lochs

The remoteness of Scotland's west coast and islands has protected the sea lochs from most of the major threats affecting coastal inlets elsewhere in Britain, particularly industrial and domestic development and its associated habitat destruction and pollution, and runoff from industry and intensive agriculture further inland. Traditionally settlements around sea lochs are small and so are the inputs of effluents from sewage and crofting activities.

Water flow is an important factor affecting sea loch wildlife and habitats. The construction of bridges and partial infilling of loch sides to support new roads involves some habitat loss but new surfaces soon recolonise are providing the water flow through the loch is not restricted.

Some aspects of fish farming can create environmental problems in sea lochs. Some of these problems have been addressed as the industry develops, such as not siting fish farms in poorly flushed areas with little current. In these conditions the seabed beneath salmon cages can become fouled with uneaten fish food and fish droppings causing the seabed to become anoxic, killing marine life immediately below the cage.

Other concerns are the continued use of pesticides to control infestations of sea lice and antibiotics to control fish diseases, these chemicals are also harmful to other marine life. There have been improvements in recent

Road causeway and bridge in Uist

years through management agreements between different fish farmers which has helped to control disease and hence reduce the need for chemical treatments. However effective disease controls which do not damage other marine life are still needed.

There is also concern over the use of certain fishing methods in the sea lochs. Trawling and dredging of the seabed can damage marine communities of both commercial and conservation value as sea lochs are important settlement and nursery areas for young fish and shellfish. The year-round closure of some sea lochs to trawling and dredging would allow stocks to recover and allow greater use of the sea lochs for less damaging static fisheries such as potting and for shellfish culture.